CW00952035

CLASSIC LANDF                    OF THE

# BRECON
# BEACONS

# CLASSIC LANDFORMS OF THE

# BRECON BEACONS

## RICHARD SHAKESBY
### University of Wales Swansea

*Series editors*
## Christopher Green, Michael Naish
## and Sally Naish

Published by the Geographical Association
in conjunction with the
British Geomorphological Research Group

**Geographical
Association**

THE BRITISH GEOMORPHOLOGICAL RESEARCH GROUP

# PREFACE

Geomorphologists study landforms and the processes that create and modify them. The results of their work, published as they invariably are in specialist journals, usually remain inaccessible to the general public. We should like to put that right. Scattered across the landscapes of England, Wales, Scotland and Ireland there are many beautiful and striking landforms which delight the eye of the general public and are also visited by educational parties from schools, colleges and universities. Our aim in producing this series of guides is to make modern explanations of these classic landforms available to all, in a style and format that will be easy to use in the field. We hope that an informed understanding of the origins of the features will help the visitor to enjoy the landscape all the more.

Encouraged by the success of the first edition of the Classic Landform Guides we are pleased to introduce this new edition, enhanced by colour photographs, new illustrations and with the valuable addition of 1:50,000 map extracts by kind permission of the Education Team, Ordnance Survey. The relevant map for the area covered in this book is Ordnance Survey 1:50,000 Landranger sheet 160 (Brecon Beacons/Bannau Brycheiniog). Please refer to the current Ordnance Survey Index for details of the relevant 1:25,000 sheets.

**Christopher Green** *Royal Holloway, University of London*
**Michael Naish and Sally Naish** *Hayes, Kent*

ISBN 1 84377 016 4
This edition first published 2002.
Published by the Geographical Association, 160 Solly Street, Sheffield S1 4BF.
The views expressed in this publication are those of the author and do not necessarily represent those of the Geographical Association.
The Geographical Association is a registered charity: no 313129.

# CONTENTS

## Safety and consideration for grazing animals

Visitors should be well prepared and aware of the potential dangers. The green rolling topography may appear free of danger, but the weather can change rapidly. With few signposts or distinctive landmarks, ill-prepared walkers can become quickly disoriented in mist. A good map and compass are essential. Many of the escarpments are steep and have loose friable bedrock outcrops. Warm, windproof and waterproof clothing should always be taken and good walking boots worn. Do not disturb livestock. Keep dogs under control. Information can be obtained from the National Park Information Centre in Brecon (Tel: 01874 623156) or from the website (www.breconbeacons.org).

*Cover photograph:* Llyn y Fan Fach with the Pwll yr Henllyn feature in the foreground.
*Photo:* Richard Shakesby.
*Frontispiece:* Brecon Beacons view. *Photo:* Richard Shakesby.

**Acknowledgements**
The author thanks Nicola Jones, Anna Ratcliffe and Alan Cutliffe for their
help in producing the illustrative material and John Matthews for invaluable
discussion about the origins of the features described in this guide.
Maps reproduced from Ordnance Survey 1:50,000 Landranger mapping.
Reproduced by kind permission of Ordnance Survey© Crown Copyright NC/02/12354.

*Copy Editing:* Rose Pipes

*Illustrations:* Paul Coles

*Series design concept:* Quarto Design, Huddersfield

*Design and typesetting:* Arkima Ltd, Leeds

*Printed and bound* at Stanley Press, Dewsbury

# INTRODUCTION

The Brecon Beacons National Park contains arguably the most spectacular upland scenery in southern Britain. It boasts the highest Old Red Sandstone summit in England and Wales (Pen y Fan, 886m), with a number of other prominent peaks exceeding 600m. Below many of the impressive escarpments (Figure 1), particularly those with a north, north-easterly or easterly aspect, lie accumulations of mainly angular rock fragments arranged in arcs, almost straight ridges or groups of ridges and irregular mounds. These enigmatic landforms mark the outer limits of small glaciers or perennial snowbeds, which developed during a short cold period that lasted for about 1500 years, and ended as recently as *c.* 11,500 years ago. During

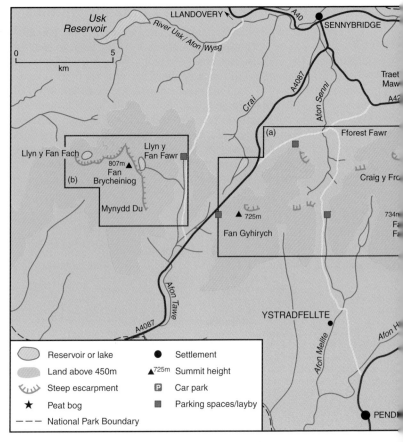

this time, much of the winter precipitation fell as snow and summers were much cooler than today. This guide describes these landforms and discusses some of the evidence for their age and possible origins.

## Geological background

The Brecon Beacons are carved out of Devonian Old Red Sandstone (ORS), which here forms the most prominent of a series of north-facing scarps along the northern borders of the South Wales Coalfield (Figure 2). The stepped appearance of the ORS strata on the steep scarps reflects alternations of more resistant brown sandstones and less resistant red marls (together forming the so-called Brownstones), which are in total some 350-420m thick. The most resistant ORS strata in the area comprise quartzitic grits and conglomerates (the so-called Plateau Beds). They form thin outcrops (usually less than 30m thick) with a shallow southerly dip on the highest summits and explain the table-like form of a number of them (e.g. Pen y Fan).

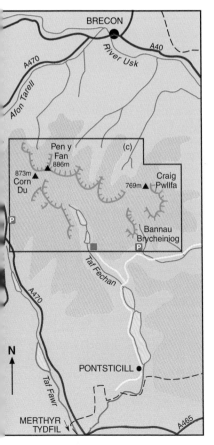

*Figure 1: Brecon Beacons National Park:* location and access. *For features considered in detail in this guide see (a) Figure 6, (b) Figure 11 and (c) Figure 14.*

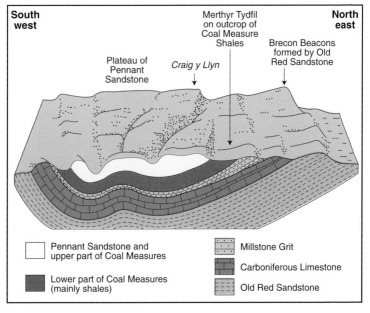

*Figure 2: The simplified geological structure of the eastern part of the South Wales Coalfield. After: Whittow, 1992.*

## Glacial history

There is some evidence for at least eight major glaciations affecting Britain during the Pleistocene (Table 1). The record of cold and warm periods locked in the sediments that have steadily accumulated on the deep ocean floors suggests that there were certainly many more, but since glacier ice is such a powerful erosive agent, much of the evidence in formerly glaciated terrain has been lost. In the Brecon Beacons, the glacial deposits are almost certainly of no greater age than the last (Devensian) glaciation, which reached its maximum around 20,000 years ago. By about 15,400 years ago, deglaciation occurred in Britain and temperatures similar to those of today were experienced. Once the supporting ice cover had gone, steepened valley sides and escarpments of upland areas experienced a comparatively brief but pronounced period of instability with rockfalls, landslides and other active slope processes. About 12,900 years ago, however, temperatures in north-west Europe dropped once more and glaciers and ice caps developed in upland Britain only to disappear again by 11,500 years ago. Plant and animal remains preserved in sediments dated to this so-called Loch Lomond Stadial (Table 1), have enabled a picture to be built up of the prevailing conditions. They indicate that much of Britain was suddenly plunged into **tundra**-like (so-called **periglacial**) conditions during this short interval. In the Brecon Beacons, the tree cover that had developed in the preceding warm interlude (Windermere **Interstadial**; *c.* 15,400-

Table 1: Simplified Quaternary chronology

| Period | Epoch | Age in years[a] | Stages and substages | Climatic characteristics | Events in Brecon Beacons |
|---|---|---|---|---|---|
| QUATERNARY | HOLOCENE | | Flandrian (=post-glacial) | Temperate<br><br>Rapid warming | Wetter conditions leading to leaching of soils and development of blanket peat. Extensive forests of oak, birch and Scots Pine developing by mid-Flandrian. |
| | | 10,000 (11,500) | Loch Lomond Stadial | Cold | Development of small glaciers and perennial snowbeds beneath escarpments Periglacial conditions beyond glacier margins. |
| | PLEISTOCENE | 11,000 (12,900) | Windermere Interstadial | Temperate | Initial instability of glacially oversteepened slopes followed by stabilisation of ground surface with open habitat. |
| | | 13,000 (15,400) | Late Devensian Glaciation (= Dimlington Stadial) | Cold | Probable inundation of Brecon Beacons by an ice sheet around 20,000 years ago |
| | | 26,000 | Early and Middle Devensian | Cold, with brief temperate interludes (interstadials) | No direct evidence known in the Brecon Beacons |
| | | 122,000 | Ipswichian Interglacial | Temperate | No direct evidence in Brecon Beacons but likely to have been forested. Temperatures c. 2-3°C higher than today. |
| | | 128,000-132,000 | Alternating glacial and interglacial stages | Alternating cold and temperate | Brecon Beacons repeatedly glaciated. Repeated erosion and deposition by ice masses ranging from small glaciers up to an ice sheet in size. Periglacial conditions affected areas beyond glacial limits during glacial stages. |
| | | c. 2.5 million | | | |

Note: a. Ages up to 15,400 years ago are expressed in terms of both radiocarbon years and approximate calendar years (in brackets). (Calibration using various techniques has shown that radiocarbon years can differ substantially from calendar (i e. 'real' years), particularly for the time of interest in this guide, from the end of the Late Devensian Glaciation until the beginning of the Holocene.)

12,900 years ago) was replaced by a sparse cover of arctic-alpine shrubs, grasses and other herbs. Bare rock surfaces underwent **freeze-thaw weathering**, so that beneath steep crags large amounts of **talus** accumulated. Where there was a veneer of debris containing both finer sediment as well as rock fragments, it was often subject to slow downslope movement (solifluction) during spring and summer thaw, even on gentle slopes. Estimated climatic conditions during the Loch Lomond Stadial indicate a more marked difference between winter and summer temperatures than is the case today. The present-day mean annual temperature at sea level in South Wales is about 11°C. During the **stadial**, the mean annual temperature is estimated to have been no warmer than -1 to -4°C, with the mean temperature of the coldest month as low as -15 to -20°C or possibly colder (Isarin *et al.*, 1998). At 500m in the Brecon Beacons temperatures would have been an additional 3°C cooler. Winds would have been predominantly westerly, as at present, but conditions were probably stormier than now.

# SCARP-FOOT LANDFORMS: POSSIBLE ORIGINS

Reade first drew attention to the former existence of glaciers in the Brecon Beacons in 1894. In a survey of the geology of the area, Robertson (1933) referred briefly to several depositional ridges, suggesting that some were glacial **moraines** while others represented debris accumulations at the bases of large snow patches (nivation ridges or **pronival (protalus) ramparts)**. Two geomorphologists considered the origin of the features in more detail during the 1960s and 1970s (Lewis, 1966, 1970; Ellis-Gruffydd, 1972, 1977) and, although they disagreed over the origin of individual features, they maintained that they represented a mix of glacial moraines and pronival ramparts. Shakesby and Matthews (1993, 1996) argued, however, that virtually none of the ridge complexes represented a pronival rampart, nearly all being formed by glacial action. They also argued that landsliding had contributed directly to the most intricate ridge complex described in this guide and may well have helped to make available large amounts of debris for incorporation by glaciers into other moraines.

For those unfamiliar with the sizes of glaciers in present-day glaciated areas, the spaces between many of the scarp-foot landforms and the corresponding scarps might be thought to be too small and hence too shallow for the development of glacier ice. Figure 3 shows generalised cross-sections of the scarp sites and associated depositional features in the Brecon Beacons together with a cross-section of an actual glacier in Norway drawn at the same scale. Clearly, a glacial origin cannot be ruled out for most sites on the basis of insufficient depth for glacier ice development. Quite the contrary, many Brecon Beacons sites offer greater depths for glacier ice development than is the case for the Norwegian glacier and since many must be floored by appreciable quantities of post-glacial debris, the bedrock basin in which the glacier would have developed must be even larger than depicted. The possibility of a glacial origin for many of the features is consequently strong.

## Glacier formation

Glaciers comprise mainly crystalline ice created when surface snow is buried progressively deeper by successive snowfalls and compressed by the pressure of overlying layers. The change from snow to glacier ice can take place at a depth of as little as 15m but more typically it is 20-30m for **warm-based glaciers**. To develop, a glacier must have an input of snow sufficient to overcome the combined losses due to melting and evaporation.

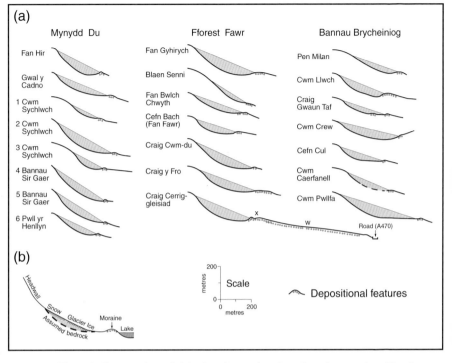

***Figure 3: Cross-sections of:*** *(a) selected scarp-foot sites where there are depositional ridges described in this guide (Note: potential maximum depths of snow or ice are indicated by lines connecting the ridges to escarpment summits), and (b) a present day small glacier at Skauthoebreen, Norway, is shown at the same scale for comparison. After: Clark and Lewis, 1951.*

If a glacier lies on a slope it will deform and, if its temperature is close to that of melting, it will also slide over its bed. The smallest glaciers occupy sheltered locations beneath escarpments in upland areas. During the Loch Lomond Stadial, only small glaciers of this type were able to survive in the higher parts of the Brecon Beacons and then only where conditions were particularly favourable. In addition to sufficiently low mean annual temperatures and a sufficient input of snow, shading is clearly an important factor. Thus in the Brecon Beacons during the Loch Lomond Stadial, important factors were:

i.   the orientation of the Old Red Sandstone escarpment towards the north-east,

ii.  the existence of amphitheatre-shaped bedrock hollows (**cirques** or **corries**) indenting the scarp face, and

iii. the proximity of a large upland plateau from which snow could be drifted by the prevailing wind into the protected lee of the escarpment (Figure 4).

# Moraine formation

Freeze-thaw weathered rock fragments from the lateral margins and backwall can fall onto the surface of a glacier and become buried by snow, eventually to be carried within the glacier ice. Some fragments may ultimately come into contact with the bedrock or other particles abrading them and producing **striations**. Many rock fragments in small glaciers, however, may well be carried within the ice or perhaps move across the glacier's steep icy surface and become deposited at the margin in more or less their original angular forms. Where the glacier margin remains stable, this dumped material can build up into a ridge and/or a series of mounds called a moraine. A newly attained stable glacier margin will produce a new ridge and/or series of mounds, so that moraine complexes may comprise more than one ridge (Figure 5a). Movement tends to be greatest near the centre of the glacier and least towards the lateral margins so that moraines are often **arcuate** in plan, reflecting the extension of the glacier in a tongue. A highly active glacier has a good supply of snow combined with rapid melting, which can balance out to provide a stable glacier margin and build a large moraine rapidly where the supply of erodible material is plentiful.

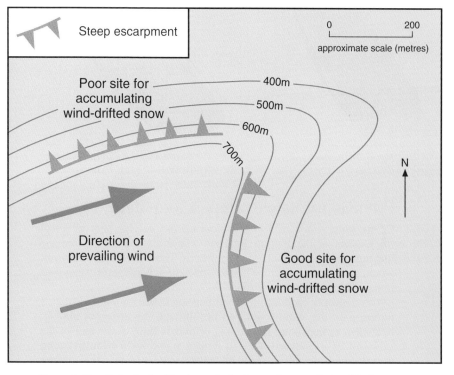

*Figure 4: Hypothetical upland landscape in the Brecon Beacons National Park.*
*This indicates escarpment sites both well suited and less well suited to the accumulation of wind-drifted snow.*

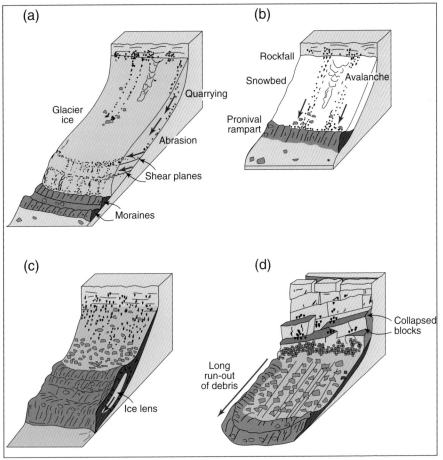

*Figure 5: Simplified forms and mechanisms of formation of: (a) a glacial moraine, (b) a pronival rampart, (c) a rock glacier, and (d) a landslide (rock avalanche).*

## Pronival (protalus) rampart formation

The same kinds of factors favouring the development of small glaciers in the Brecon Beacons would also have favoured the maintenance of large perennial snowbeds. These snowbeds, however, would not have developed into glaciers where snow thickness remained insufficient.

With a steeply-inclined snowbed beneath a steep rock face, debris falling onto the snow could end up, through the action of sliding, bouncing, avalanching, landsliding or **debris flow**, at the foot of the snowbed. If a snowbed were to remain stable for a relatively long period, a considerable quantity of debris could build up in this manner leading to the formation of a ridge, known as a pronival (alternatively, protalus) rampart (Figure 5b). Limited sliding of a snowbed has also recently been shown to produce minor ridges, and solifluction and other processes have been observed transporting relatively small amounts of sediment beneath perennial snowbeds in Norway (Shakesby, 1997). Different marginal positions of the snowbed can produce benches or multiple ridges. There are, therefore, two key characteristics concerning the location and sediments of fossil pronival ramparts that usually help to distinguish them from glacial moraines: the former are located where the depth of perennial snow accumulation would have been too little to allow conversion of the snow to glacier ice and they tend to lack abraded and striated rock fragments characteristic of transport at the base of a glacier.

## Rock glacier formation

Although sometimes neglected in introductory landform texts, rock glaciers are surprisingly common in certain mountain periglacial environments. Talus-foot or valley-wall rock glaciers form benches or lobes of very slow-moving talus that can spread out like thick porridge onto the valley floor (Figure 5c). Movement by slow deformation is dependent on an ice core, series of ice lenses, or refrozen snowmelt and/or rain that forms an ice-rock mix within the talus. When the ice finally melts, the talus usually settles into an upstanding mass of ridged debris. Rock glaciers require low mean annual temperatures, only a thin winter snow cover so that cold winter air can penetrate deep into the talus, and a plentiful supply of debris from the slopes above. These requirements might have been met at some sites in the Brecon Beacons during the Loch Lomond Stadial.

## Landslide formation

Glacial erosion in uplands can cause many slopes to be very steep ('oversteepened') so that once the support of the ice has gone, the slopes may for a period become susceptible to landsliding (Figure 5d). Cold temperatures fluctuating around 0°C, a plentiful supply of water from melting snow and a well-jointed bedrock (as is the case with Old Red Sandstone) would have left certain locations particularly susceptible to sudden rapid rockfalls or slides immediately following ice-sheet melting around 15,400 years ago. Similar conditions may have existed again at the end of the Loch Lomond Stadial around 11,500 years ago. Certainly, there are clear examples of landslides in the Brecon Beacons where glaciers did not develop during the Loch Lomond Stadial (e.g. Fan Dringarth – see Figure 6, page 16) and they are characterised by splays or tongues of debris forming ridges and mounds of debris.

# FFOREST FAWR AREA

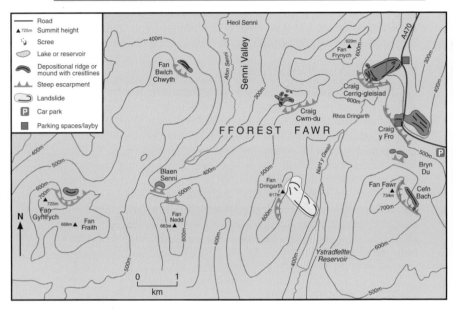

**Figure 6: Fforest Fawr:** *depositional ridges and mounds (see Figure 1 for location within the Brecon Beacons National Park).*

In the Fforest Fawr area (Figure 6), which has peaks up to 734m at Fan Fawr (SN 970194), 663m at Fan Nedd (SN 914184) and 725m at Fan Gyhirych (SN 881191), there are seven or possibly eight sets of depositional ridges. All but one of the features occur below scarps overlooking Glyn Tarell and the Senni Valley. The main A470 road from Merthyr Tydfil to Brecon passes along Glyn Tarell which was occupied and shaped by ice during successive major glaciations including the most recent one (Devensian). Two glacial cirques (Craig Cerrig-gleisiad (SN 964220) and Craig y Fro (SN 974207)) close to this road show evidence of occupation by small glaciers during the Loch Lomond Stadial. The road follows the base of the backwall of one of these cirques below the crags of Craig y Fro while the other cirque, below Craig Cerrig-gleisiad, lies a short walk from it. Neither the form of these cirques nor that of the depositional hummocks and ridges within them are classic 'textbook' examples, yet from associated peat deposits they have yielded crucial indirect evidence of the likely age of all the depositional features described in this guide.

N

*Photo 1: Vertical aerial image of Craig Cerrig-gleisiad cirque and its depositional
landforms. Compare with Figure 7. Copyright: MOD.*

# Craig Cerrig-gleisiad

A spectacular hollow has been cut southwards and westwards into
generally north-sloping topography (Photo 1). The cirque thus
lacks a pronounced sidewall on the northern side and consequently
does not have the classic 'armchair' form often quoted in textbooks.
Instead it more closely resembles an L-shape of steep crags when seen
from above. The magnificent southern crags of the cirque form the
steepest and most impressive part of the headwall, which rises to a
maximum of about 160m above the cirque floor. The crags are

serrated by a number of deep gullies. At the lower ends of the biggest of these gullies lie large **debris cones**, most of which are well vegetated and hence inactive but they also include some fresh talus. The headwall turns abruptly towards the north-west to form about a 400m stretch of the western headwall (Photo 2). This comprises collapsed backward-tilting bedrock blocks and tension cracks in the bedrock (Figure 7). Northwards of the western headwall, the headwall degrades into a low-angled (14°) slope with a vegetated, broadly triangular-shaped area of irregular hummocky terrain with ridges aligned approximately parallel to the contours. At the base of this triangular area are distinct ridges (including ridge Z in Figure 7), which rise steeply from the valley floor. On the cirque floor, a complex set of hummocks and ridges occurs, which are best appreciated from the air (Photo 1). For convenience, distinct groups of these landforms are labelled W, X and Y on Figure 7. Area X comprises mounds that form mostly sub-parallel ridges trending broadly north-west to south-east and rising some 10-20m above the cirque floor. The boundary of this area facing the headwall is abrupt and steep. The mounds are highest at the north-western end adjacent to the 6m-deep peat bog (P). The tongue-shaped area (W) extends for more than 1km from the top of the western headwall. Its central area has an indistinct undulating surface but on its lateral margins there are marked mounds and ridges, the heights of which are exaggerated by stream downcutting on the outer edges. The northern margin is marked by a single ridge rising up to 7m above the adjacent tongue. The southern margin is more pronounced and forms a series of

*Photo 2: The western headwall of Craig Cerrig-gleisiad cirque* showing backward-tilted bedrock block (note figure to left of photo for scale). Tension cracks occur to the right of the fence at the extreme top right of the photo.

mounds up to about 10m above the adjoining tongue. Bounding the peat bog (P) on its north-eastern side is a curved, broad 2m-high ridge.

Until the mid-1990s, ideas on the origin of these features included: (i) two glacial advances, one in the Loch Lomond Stadial and one earlier (Lewis, 1966, 1970); (ii) ice-sheet deposition followed by restricted Loch Lomond Stadial cirque glacier formation (Ellis-Gruffydd, 1972); (iii) development entirely within the Loch Lomond Stadial by a cirque glacier of very variable size that initially formed the ridges in W and later those in X (Robertson, 1989). Recently, however, inspection of the headwall geological structure and detailed mapping and analysis of the sediments has suggested that none of these explanations is satisfactory and that in part an origin by non-glacial means is indicated (Shakesby and Matthews, 1996). One problem with a wholly glacial origin is that although the form of the cirque is not unlike that of others with moraines in the Brecon Beacons, the ridges in other moraine complexes are closely-spaced, suggesting that when active the glaciers that formed the ridges varied little in size. The low-angled cirque floor and the comparatively small accumulation area for wind-drifted snow are not the sorts of conditions normally associated with a glacier varying markedly in size in response to variations in snow input. Variability in extent is more characteristic of a glacier with a very large accumulation area feeding into a comparatively narrow valley.

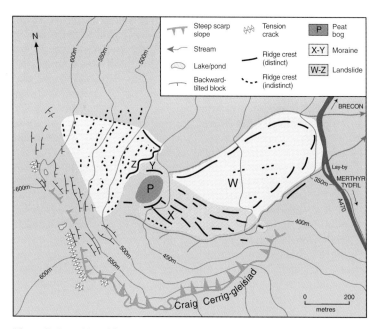

*Figure 7: Depositional features in Craig Cerrig-gleisiad cirque.*
Letters indicate sites referred to in the text. After: Shakesby and Matthews, 1996.

There can be little doubt that the ridges in area X are glacial in origin. This is indicated by the abraded and slightly rounded stones found in the mounds. More critically, up to 32% of these stones have striations (Photo 3). Area W, on the other hand, seems to have had a non-glacial origin, as a type of landslide known as a rock avalanche formed by the sudden collapse of the western headwall. Where the vertical fall of rock is large, such landslides can have a large **run-out** distance even over comparatively flat ground. Such landslides typically have upstanding lateral and terminal ridges because debris is brought rapidly to a halt at the margins. Inspection of bedrock bedding planes around the backwall shows why the landslide originated in the western part. The bedding planes are tilted towards the south-east at about 15°. Their declination into the southern headwall causes it to be stable despite the steepness. Along the western headwall, however, the bedding planes dip at an angle away from the rock face. Not surprisingly, glacial oversteepening left this slope liable to collapse once the ice sheets disappeared about 15,400 years ago, as indicated by the backward-tilted blocks and tension cracks that are still clear today. Calculations show that a wedge-shaped area measuring about 270m by 100m at the top and tapering to the foot of the scarp removed from the western wall can more than account for the volume of deposits in W and X.

Beyond the western wall, the slope of the ground into the cirque and the dip of the bedding planes virtually coincide. This accounts for the formation of the triangular-shaped area and ridge Z, which represent 'rucking' of a layer of rock that has slipped down a bedding plane.

The origin of Y is difficult to explain. If it is a moraine, the steepness of the slope at the north-western end of area X next to the peat bog implies that glacier ice was present on the site of the peat bog (forming ridge Y) at the same time as the glacier was forming the ridges in X. If this is correct, a possible explanation for the development of such a small, subsidiary ice 'tongue' extending across P lies in the importance of wind-drifting in supplying much of the snow input. It may be that the site was well positioned to receive snow funnelled during south-westerly winds along the valley west of, and beheaded by, the western headwall of the cirque.

The proposed sequence of formation of the features in the cirque is shown in Figure 8. At some point after the cirque emerged from beneath an ice sheet cover at the end of the Devensian (Figure 8a) landsliding occurred (Figure 8b). During the Loch Lomond Stadial, some of the landslide deposits (together with any newly eroded material) were reworked by a small glacier to form moraine ridges (Figure 8c). Since the glacier melted (by about 11,500 years ago), the depositional landforms have remained comparatively 'fresh' with peat accumulating in the shallow depression behind ridge Y (Figure 8d).

## Dating evidence

Traeth Mawr (SN 967257), a 5m-deep peat bog about 1km south-west of the Visitor Centre (SN 977263) and 3.5km north of Craig Cerrig-

**Photo 3: Abraded rock fragment with striations** *from a moraine ridge in area X, Craig Cerrig-gleisiad cirque.*

gleisiad (Figure 1) lies outside the limit of Loch Lomond Stadial ice and has yielded a radiocarbon-dated, pollen-bearing peat sequence extending back through post-glacial times to the Stadial, which is represented by silts and clays reflecting **slopewash** and solifluction processes. Below these silts and clays are peats and organic muds representing the preceding temperate Windermere Interstadial (Figure 9a). In contrast, because it lies inside the Stadial limit, the 6m-deep peat-filled hollow (P) in Craig Cerrig-gleisiad cirque only has post-glacial peat deposits (Figure 9b). Here, the lowermost organic muds and peats record vegetation change following cold stadial conditions with, first, juniper and birch superseded later by hazel, oak, pine and elm, which then declined as oak and elder expanded (Walker, 1980, 1982a). The radiocarbon date of *c.* 10,900 years **BP** (about 12,800 calendar years) marking the beginning of post-glacial peat development at Craig Cerrig-gleisiad is rather older than was anticipated, a radiocarbon date of about 10,000 (11,500 calendar years) being expected. It seems likely that this 'old' date is explained by contamination from the weathering of cornstone conglomerate rock, which contains carbon of extreme age. (A report by Bowen (1999) of a calendar date of about 15,000 years for debris in tongue W (on Figure 7) in Craig Cerrig-gleisiad cirque tallies with a landslide origin immediately after deglaciation.)

## Access

Car parking for Craig Cerrig-gleisiad cirque is possible in a lay-by on the A470 at SN 972223. A footpath leads from here up to the cwm. Consult signs on the footpath for detailed information on rights of way. Rare flora and fauna found on the steep slopes of Craig Cerrig-gleisiad has resulted in the site being designated a National Nature Reserve. **Do not climb these slopes.**

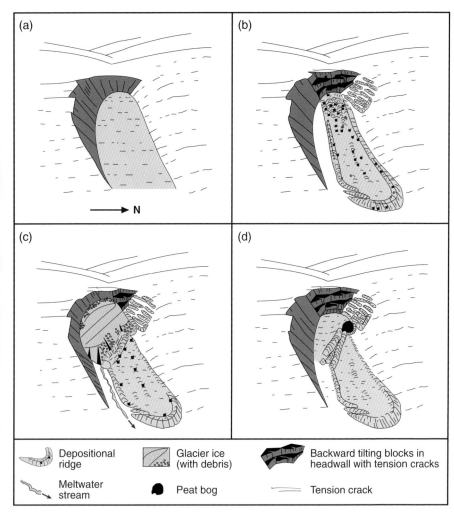

*Figure 8: Simplified reconstruction of probable stages in the formation of the depositional landforms in Craig Cerrig-gleisiad cirque, as viewed from the east: (a) immediately after ice sheet decay, the western part of the backwall remained intact, (b) after some time, landsliding affected the western and north-western parts of the headwall, (c) during the Loch Lomond Stadial a small glacier reworked some landslide material, and (d) during the last 11,500 years since the glacier melted, little has changed other than the accumulation of a peat bog in a hollow enclosed by a morainic ridge.*

## Craig y Fro

Craig y Fro (SN 973207) (Figure 9c) lies *c.* lkm south of the eastern end of Craig Cerrig-gleisiad, with the main A470 road following the base of the headwall. The prominent depositional forms (up to 10m high) below the headwall are regarded as glacial in origin and

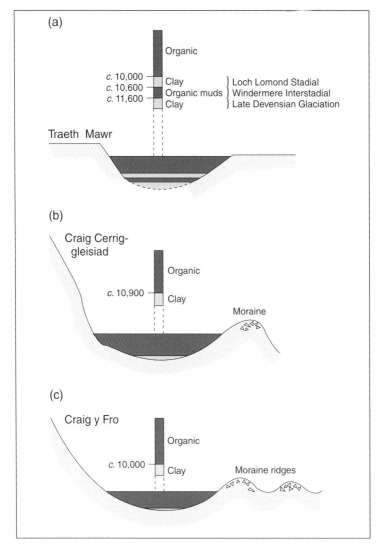

*Figure 9: Schematic of the sediment types and approximate radiocarbon dates determined from peat bogs: (a) outside, and (b-c) inside the Loch Lomond Stadial glacial limits in the Brecon Beacons (see Figure 1 for locations).*

comprise a series of compound parallel ridges similar to the inner moraine complex in Craig Cerrig-gleisiad cirque. There are prominent breaks of slope at the base of the outermost ridge and on the inside slope of the innermost ridge. The latter runs upslope as a lateral moraine to the north-west (and is cut through by the A470 road) but is separated from the headwall to the south-east by a dry channel which may represent a former glacial meltwater route. The moraine complex comprises sandy material with subangular stones, some of which can be matched with rock types from Craig y Fro itself. No striated stones have been reported, although there is every likelihood that they exist.

The well-developed moraine complex at first sight seems to be out of place below the comparatively low, unimpressive escarpment. The explanation must lie in the large plateau of Rhos Dringarth (SN 960215) to the west (Figure 6) offering an extensive accumulation area from which snow could be wind-drifted into the lee of the escarpment. The better lateral moraine development on the north-west side of the glacier (cut through when constructing the A470 road) can simply be related to a greater supply of debris to the glacier margin here as a result of a more actively eroded north-west section of the headwall which is consequently steeper and more rugged.

Up to 4.5m of organic muds and peat were found by Walker (1980) in the peat-filled hollow inside the moraine. A radiocarbon date from the basal organic muds gave an age very close to 10,000 radiocarbon years BP (11,500 calendar years), suggesting the glacier had melted by then. Pollen extracted from the peat showed a similar pattern of post-glacial vegetation change to that already described for Craig Cerrig-gleisiad cirque and Traeth Mawr (Walker, 1982a,b).

## Bryn Du

About 1km north-west of Bryn Du (SN 979195) lies a single, irregular and poorly developed ridge (up to 3m high), which is slightly arcuate and seems to follow the curvature of a small (25m) scarp (SN 970200) just above Craig y Fro (Figure 6). This was interpreted as a pronival rampart (Lewis, 1966), but given the small size of the scarp this seems unlikely. The origin of the ridge remains uncertain.

## Cefn Bach (Fan Fawr)

About 1.5km south of Craig y Fro lies the broad summit of Fan Fawr (734m, SN 9619). Its eastern side has been eroded to form a curving scarp up to about 80m in height. Below this is a single arcuate ridge up to 11m high with an undulating crest line known as Cefn Bach ('Little Hill') (SN 974192) (Photo 4). It curves around to join the foot of the scarp at its southern end. Near its centre, this feature lies some 200m from the scarp. Originally thought to be a glacial moraine, it was subsequently interpreted as a pronival rampart, but a glacial origin seems clear in view of:

i.   the large distance of the feature from such a relatively small scarp, making it difficult to see how material subject to freeze-thaw weathering near the top of the scarp could move by gravity over the snowbed all the way to the ridge;

ii.  the ample cross-sectional depth for glacier development; and

iii. the manner in which the ridge curves around to meet the escarpment at its lower, southern end, which suggests glacier movement in that direction rather than accumulation of debris around a static snowbed.

24

*Photo 4: Cefn Bach moraine (left) and Fan Fawr escarpment (right).*

## Craig Cwm-du (Figure 10)

The Craig Cwm-du valley is aligned in an east to west direction and hangs some 120m above the Senni Valley. The mouth of Nant Cwm Du (SN 940215) is marked by a low, broad, depositional ridge through which the stream has carved a small gorge. The escarpment of Craig Cwm-du (SN 945213) is aligned roughly west-south-west to east-north-east and rises some 165m above the floor of the valley. The lower slopes are covered with talus cones and deep gullies leading up to **debris chutes** which notch the top of the scarp.

The depositional hummocks and ridge remnants north-west of the escarpment are regarded as glacial in origin but they have been considerably modified by stream action, which is clearly indicated by well-developed low terraces of mainly subrounded and subangular stones. Although the glacier appears to have developed beneath the scarp its former extent is unclear. Two isolated hummocks (A and B in Figure 10) could represent remnants of a former outer moraine but, if so, stream erosion has destroyed most of the rest of the feature. The clearest, unmistakable moraine fragment (SN 941214) climbs up the western footslope of the scarp and was formed by a small glacier that nestled against the scarp. The stream appears to cut through more than one ridge immediately downstream of the bridge. At some stage, the broad ridge (D), probably also a moraine, may have dammed a lake. The latter's former existence is indicated by red and light grey, fine, layered sediments which can be seen in an exposure near the bridge (SN 943215). The overflow route from this lake may well have been via the small steep dry valley (X in Figure 10) some 200m west of the present route of Nant Du. Although the scarp is impressive and backed by a large plateau, at least part of the reason for the comparatively small extent of the glacier (discounting the possibility

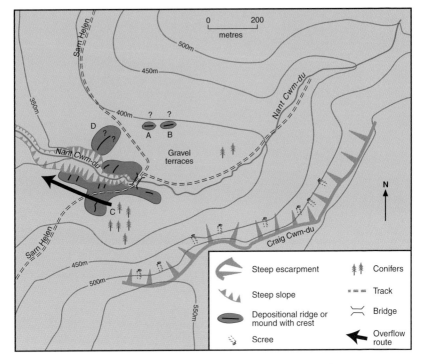

**Figure 10:** *The location of depositional features in the Craig Cwm-du site. Letters indicate features referred to in the text.*

that it extended as far as hummocks A and B) must lie in the unfavourable alignment of the headwall. It would have allowed south-westerly winds to scour out snow accumulating beneath the scarp. Only winds from the south, therefore, could lead to effective wind-drifting of snow into the site.

### Access

The Craig Cwm-du site lies on a footpath that follows a track (Sarn Helen), formerly a Roman road. Limited roadside parking is possible at the southern end of this track (SN 925184).

## Fan Bwlch Chwyth

Perched on the western flanks of the Senni Valley about 1km downvalley from Craig Cwm-du lies a pronounced north-east facing hollow backed by a *c.* 120m high curved backwall with its abandoned quarry. Two distinct arcuate depositional ridges with undulating crests enclose a peaty depression. The outer ridge (SN 916224) stands up to 12m above the sloping ground beyond the moraine, with angles on the outer slope of up to 26°. Angles on the inner slopes of the moraine and the height above the surrounding ground are considerably less. Exposures in the moraine show

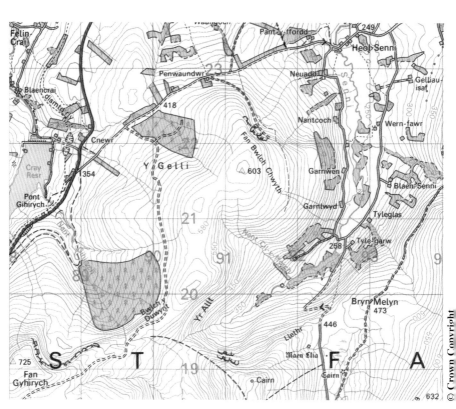

© Crown Copyright

subangular material in a mainly sand and silt sediment. These excellently preserved ridges are unmistakably glacial moraines, even having enclosed hollows representing locations where lumps of ice became buried (so-called **kettle holes**). The glacier would have been nourished by snow blowing off the broad plateau expanses to the south-west by the prevailing winds.

### Access

Car parking is possible at Penwaundwr (SN 907228). From the road take the footpath leading south-east, which leads to the Fan Bwlch Chwyth feature.

## Blaen Senni

At a height of about 400m, beneath a subsidiary escarpment (SN 910194) near the steep head of Senni Valley, lies a small but conspicuous arcuate depositional ridge that rises little more than 1m above the surrounding ground (Figure 6). The ridge might appear surprisingly small in view of the size and steepness of the scarp. The arcuate plan form of the ridge suggests formation involving movement away from the scarp and thus a glacial origin, but the cross-sectional area of the hollow is small so that a pronival rampart origin cannot be ruled out (Figure 3). If a glacier existed here it was a small one that was not capable of building a large moraine and hence was probably not very active. This could be explained by the northerly aspect of the scarp and the tendency for westerly winds to scour snow out from the comparatively poorly-protected valley-side position of this feature (see Figure 4). Whether a glacier or a snowbed occupied this site, it would have been poorly-nourished, so making the input of snow low but, on the other hand, melting would have been at a minimum because the site is comparatively well shaded.

## Fan Gyhirych

The cirque north-east of the triangular, flat-topped summit of Fan Gyhirych (725m) (SN 881191) has a well developed western, curving headwall and a southern headwall that declines in steepness towards the east. Like Craig Cerrig-gleisiad cirque, the nature of the surrounding topography has meant that a northern sidewall is absent. In view of its close resemblance to Craig Cerrig-gleisiad cirque one might expect to find an equally impressive suite of glacial depositional features, but this is not so. Instead there is a single, subdued, broad crescentic ridge (SN 887194), which follows the curve of the backwall at a distance of more than 200m. Scattered on the surface of this ridge are many **erratics** derived from the Plateau Beds that cap the summit.

It has been suggested that the ridge is a pronival rampart in view mainly of the way it parallels the backwall, includes erratic material from the summit and lacks lateral ridges. On the other hand, the ridge lies a long way from the escarpment so that material would have to have moved over a very shallow-angled snowbed surface (19°) for a distance of some 400m to reach the ridge (Figure 3). For these reasons, a glacial origin seems more likely. The isolated, upstanding nature of the Fan Gyhirych cirque with its steep western face may have caused much of the snow blown by the prevailing westerly winds to be moved around rather than into the cirque. Craig Cerrig-gleisiad cirque, in contrast, has gently sloping ground on its western side allowing large quantities of wind-drifted snow to accumulate in the depression. Ill-nourished by drifting snow, the Fan Gyhirych glacier might well have been comparatively inactive. If this were the case, the glacier would not have been vigorous and hence not very erosive, which would explain the unimposing nature of the ridge. Alternatively, the glacier may have varied more in extent than the other glaciers, thus explaining the less pronounced form of the moraine, or perhaps there was less landslide debris at Fan Gyhirych than at Craig Cerrig-gleisiad.

Access

Viewpoints for both the Blaen Senni and Fan Gyhirych features can be accessed via a footpath that joins the A4067 at SN 870194, where roadside parking is possible.

# MYNYDD DU

At the foot of the north- and east-facing scarps of Mynydd Du (or Black Mountain) (Figure 11) lies a range of magnificent depositional features of presumed Loch Lomond Stadial age. The escarpment extends for some 7km. From Fan Hir in the south at an altitude of about 450m (SN 840180) there is a steady climb northwards to the highest point at Fan Brycheiniog (802m) (SN 826218) which overlooks Llyn y Fan Fawr (SN 830216). The escarpment continues northwards to the narrow spur at Fan Foel (781m) (SN 822224), where it turns abruptly to the south-west then generally westwards, reaching high points at Picws Du (749m) (SN 812218) and Waun Lefrith (677m) (SN 798215). The escarpment finally curves around the western end of Llyn y Fan Fach (SN 803217) and peters out. The scarps here are scarred by magnificent gullies with their associated debris flows (Statham, 1976). Nine sets of depositional features can be identified below the scarps.

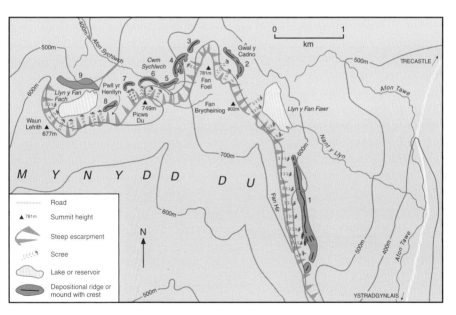

*Figure 11: Mynydd Du: depositional ridges and mounds. Numbers indicate features referred to in the text (see Figure 1 for location).*

29

# Fan Hir

Immediately east of the Fan Hir escarpment is the most striking and enigmatic of the Mynydd Du group of depositional features (Photo 5; feature 1 on Figure 11). For much of its length, the ridge rises up to 30m above the gully that separates it from the scarp of Fan Hir, which itself rises a further 120m above the gully. It is 1.2km long and runs mostly parallel to the scarp with an uninterrupted crest line. The ridge becomes lower at its northern end and degrades into 2m- to 3m-high mounds. Towards its southern end, the crest becomes broader, lower, hummocky and curved with peat-filled hollows (Figure 12). At the southern end, the ridge increases in height, becomes sharp-crested once more and curves to meet the scarp (SN 836196). Here, it has been breached, leaving a steep-sided gorge occupied today by a small stream. Two small (about 1-2 m high and 150m long) parallel ridges, marked X and Y on Figure 12, occur within the gully. The main ridge rests in part on a bedrock ridge. This, together with stream downcutting in the gully, means that the size of the depositional ridge is probably exaggerated, though nevertheless impressive.

Until the early 1990s, this magnificent feature was viewed as a pronival rampart, mainly because it reportedly lay entirely parallel to the escarpment (suggesting formation associated with a static snowbed rather than a mobile glacier) and was at the foot of a steep escarpment, implying insufficient room for glacier development. Detailed work at the site in the early 1990s, however, showed it was unmistakably glacial in origin (Shakesby and Matthews, 1993). The

**Photo 5: The southern end of the Fan Hir moraine.** *It climbs partway up the escarpment and has been cut through by stream action. Note sheep for scale.*

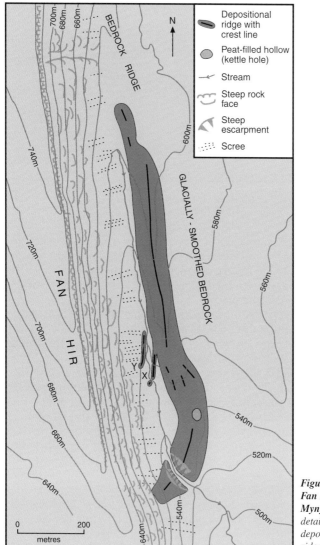

*Figure 12:*
*Fan Hir,*
*Mynydd Du:*
*detail of*
*depositional*
*ridges.*

most important evidence reported was the presence in ridge sediment at the southern end of up to 20% of stones with glacial striations. On Old Red Sandstone rock surfaces, these marks are rapidly obliterated by weathering once exposed, so that survival since the Devensian ice-sheet glaciation of so many well-preserved striations on any unprotected surfaces seems highly improbable. Instead, the striations must have been formed by whatever created the ridge (i.e. a small active glacier) and became well-preserved once embedded, and therefore protected, in the fine sediment in the ridge. Other indications of glacial origin are:

*Figure 13: How the Fan Hir glacier may have appeared during the Loch Lomond Stadial, as viewed from the south-east.*

1. the 'glacial' characteristics of the ridge (curved, hummocky, climbing up the escarpment) near its southern end, which is the lower end of the feature and therefore the direction in which the glacier would have tended to move as well as generally eastwards away from the escarpment;
2. a sufficient depth to the hollow behind the ridge for glacier development (in fact, more than 50m; Figure 3);
3. enclosed hollows on the ridge near the southern end representing kettle holes (SN 837194); and
4. the improbably large amounts of erosion concentrated on rock surfaces near the top of the escarpment needed to form the ridge if it were a pronival rampart (any contribution of debris from beneath the snowbed being minimal or non-existent). In contrast, material eroded by a glacier could have been obtained from anywhere in the gap between the summit of the escarpment and the moraine.

The two small ridges (X and Y on Figure 12) probably represent brief phases of glacial readvance or stability during a general retreat. An impression of how the glacier may have looked is given in Figure 13.

## Llyn y Fan Fawr and Gŵal y Cadno

A number of writers have suggested that Llyn y Fan Fawr is dammed in part by bedrock but also partly by a series of low boulder- and peat-covered mounds representing a Loch Lomond Stadial glacial moraine. This seems doubtful for the following reasons. First, the quantity of ice necessary to fill in the gap between the scarp and the supposed moraine is very large in comparison with the amount implied by the other features along this section of scarp. Second, the site does not offer any special protection, particularly in the south, to assist snow accumulation. Third, any depositional mounds on the eastern shores of the lake are subdued by comparison with the remarkably fresh appearance of other depositional features in

***Photo 6: Looking east from Picws Du*** *towards features 3, 4 and 5 (see Figure 11) in Cwm Sychlwch, Mynydd Du.*

the vicinity. Fourth, the lake is shallow (less than 21m deep) and there are no clear signs of ridges on its bed or along the western shore below the escarpment, so that if the site was once occupied by a small glacier, it has left no trace.

Some 500m north at Gŵal y Cadno (SN 826223; feature 2 on Figure 11) is a small, but well formed arcuate ridge enclosing a peaty area developed on post-glacial accumulations of avalanche and debris flow material from the backwall. The 110m-high backwall forms a small embayment and faces north-east. The ridge stands some 9m above the ground surface beyond the ridge, but little more than 1m above the debris infill inside it. The presence of striated rock fragments that can be found in small exposures in the ridge confirms a glacial moraine origin.

## Cwm Sychlwch

There are seven features below the north-facing section of the Mynydd Du scarp, of which three occupy what has been called Cwm Sychlwch (SN 817220) in the east (Photo 6). The eastern-most ridge (SN 819227) (3 in Figure 11) lies close to the foot of the western face of Fan Foel. This is possibly a pronival rampart, given its small size and position on the lower slopes of the scarp, although a rock glacier origin is not out of the question (see feature 7, below Picws Du). Immediately west of the feature is a 6m high arcuate ridge enclosing some hummocks and ridge fragments (4 in Figure 11). The arcuate form indicates a glacial origin. The third feature (SN 816221) (5 in Figure 11) is more problematic. It is a well-formed near-linear ridge rising 6m above the surrounding almost flat ground and lies some 100m from the backwall that here forms a col over which one of the Afon Sychlwch headwaters flows. A pronival rampart origin has been suggested because of its linear plan form and lack of lateral ridges. On the other hand, its large distance from a low scarp is a problem because material would have to move over a very low-angled snowbed surface. Certainly, on the grounds of cross-section size there is no problem arguing for a glacial origin (Figure 3). Unfortunately a lack of exposures in the ridge means that the nature of the constituent material cannot be easily examined.

## Picws Du and Pwll yr Henllyn

On aerial images and from a high vantage point on Fan Foel, the small ridge (SN 814221) below the impressive north-east facing scarp of Picws Du (6 in Figure 11) is reasonably distinct. Its southern end lies close to feature 5, from where it curves to the north-west to run along the eastern bank of Afon Sychlwch. It follows the stream until the point where the escarpment changes direction sharply, where it crosses the stream and curves around towards the escarpment. It is not easy to see on the ground. Its small size beneath the 150m escarpment of Picws Du makes a pronival rampart origin probable, but no detailed work has yet been published.

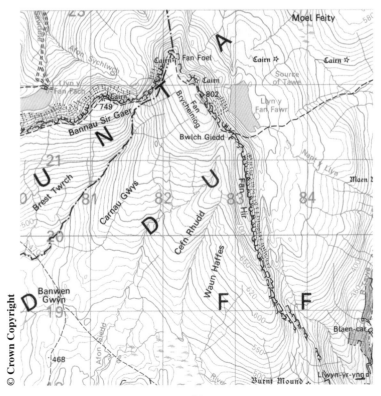

*Photo 7: The arcuate outer ridge and debris infill at the foot of the north-west facing slope below Picws Du (feature 7 in Figure 11).*

A second feature (SN 808221) (7 in Figure 11; Photo 7) lies below Picws Du at the foot of its north-west-facing slopes. It comprises a single arcuate ridge with steep outer slopes behind which is an infill of talus material brought down by debris flows from the scarp above. Small quantities of this material have been transported over the ridge at low points. The difficulty with any interpretation of this feature is explaining why so well-developed a ridge should have been formed where there are no obvious advantages for snow accumulation. On the contrary, the north-east to south-west alignment of the scarp, its poorly-developed nature and its slightly convex shape seen from above would seem to make it a poor site for accumulating wind-drifted snow. A pronival rampart origin has been suggested but seems problematic given the poor position of the site for collecting snow. For this same reason, and given the degraded character of the scarp here, a glacial origin must also be questionable. Alternatively, it may be a valley-wall or talus-foot rock glacier. For a rock glacier to develop, thick accumulations of snow would be a disadvantage; on the other hand, shading due to a northerly aspect, a plentiful supply of talus and a mean annual temperature below 0°C would be particular advantages. All these attributes would have been present at this site during the Loch Lomond Stadial. That it juts out from the base of the escarpment is typical of such rock glaciers. Problems with this interpretation are that the feature is small and there are no inner ridges visible, although these could conceivably be buried beneath the post-glacial talus infill.

*Photo 8: Pwyll yr Henllyn moraine.*

Opposite a small north-facing embayment at Pwll yr Henllyn (SN 807217) is a slightly sinuous ridge (8 in Figure 11; Photo 8), which stands up to 6-12m high, with a subsidiary ridge beyond. The ground falls quite steeply westwards across the embayment and at its western end the main ridge becomes rapidly smaller but can be traced a short distance where it curves towards the escarpment. This feature has been regarded as a pronival rampart (Ellis-Gruffydd, 1972, 1977) in view of its 'linear' form and its closeness to the escarpment, but a glacial origin seems more probable in view of its large size in relation to the escarpment, and its curved form in the west which indicates downslope glacier movement in this direction. A difficulty with this view is that the ridge becomes smaller in the supposed direction of ice movement as opposed to larger, as is the case for Cwm Crew in the Brecon Beacons (page 43-45). Nevertheless, there is sufficient cross-sectional depth at the site for the development of glacier ice (Figure 3).

## Llyn y Fan Fach

This artificially-dammed lake (SN 803217) (Photo 9 and cover) occupies a magnificent cirque with particularly well-developed western and southern walls up to about 160m high. It is well positioned to collect drifting snow as it has a north-easterly aspect and lies east of large expanses of comparatively gently-sloping terrain. A broad ridge and hummock complex is draped over the slopes on the

***Photo 9: Llyn y Fan Fach with Pwll yr Henllyn*** *featured in the middle ground.*

northern side of the lake (9 in Figure 11) but the feature is best developed near the lake outlet where hummocks stand 15-18m above the break of slope defining the outer limit of the feature. The large distance of the feature from the backwall, and the large size and favourable situation of the cirque for collecting snow, make a glacial origin unquestionable.

## Access

All the sites described in this section are on unenclosed land. Roadside car parking is possible on the minor road that joins the A4067 at SN 850172. Many of the features are best viewed from the top of the escarpment. A good route up the escarpment is via a well-used footpath (though not actually a public right of way) which leaves the minor road at SN 855224. The footpath skirts the southern end of Llyn y Fan Fawr at SN 833214. Expect to encounter small streams and bogs en route.

# BANNAU
# BRYCHEINIOG

Bannau Brycheiniog or 'Brecon Beacons' is used here to refer to the peaks and scarps (Figure 14) forming the high ground stretching east of the A470 for some 10km. Here are arguably the most spectacular glacial erosional and depositional landforms in the Brecon Beacons National Park, as well as the two highest peaks in Corn Du (873m) (SO 007214) and Pen y Fan (886m) (SO 012216) (Photo 10). Five spectacular parallel glacial **trough head** valleys (Cwm Llwch (SO 003220), Cwm Sere (SO 021218), Cwm Cynwyn (SO 034213), Cwm Oergwm (SO 042204) and Cwm Cwareli (SO 054207)) have been cut into the north-facing escarpment (Frontispiece), while the southern dip slope is less well endowed with deep valleys, the exceptions being Cwm Crew (SO 008197), Blaen Taf Fechan (SO 021200) and Blaen Caerfanell (SO 054193). There are also several crescent-shaped depressions carved into the escarpment (e.g. Cwm Pwllfa (SO 068207)). At least 10 or possibly 12 sets of depositional ridges and hummocks of presumed Loch Lomond Stadial age can be found in trough heads and escarpment indentations around this upland area. These features will be dealt with in an anti-clockwise direction beginning in the south-east.

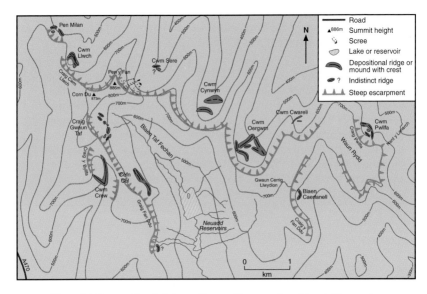

*Figure 14: Bannau Brycheiniog or Brecon Beacons: depositional ridges and mounds (see Figure 1 for location).*

*Photo 10: The table-like summits of Pen y Fan and Corn Du, Brecon Beacons.*

# Blaen Caerfanell

This site lies south of the main west to east escarpment and below the northern end of Craig y Fan Ddu (SO 054185), which marks the eastern boundary of the Gwaun Cerrig Llwydion plateau (SO 047195). The Caerfanell stream runs south across the plateau and then east over the backwall of the indentation. The backwall has an average slope of 33-35° and rises to about 660m. At a distance of between about 150m and 215m, and on a distinct bench at about 560m, lies an arcuate ridge that is well formed in the south where it is some 10m high: by contrast, in the north it rises little more than 1m or so above the surrounding ground surface. The ridge encloses a marked depression that once sheltered a now ruined farmhouse. Where the stream cuts through the ridge it provides deep exposures revealing mainly subangular and angular rock fragments embedded in fine sediment. Some of the fragments are striated, which, together with the arcuate form of the ridge and the overdeepened nature of the now infilled bedrock hollow, indicate that the ridge is a glacial moraine. The site is very favourably situated for collecting drifting snow blown off the plateau to the west.

## Cwm Pwllfa

North-east of Blaen Caerfanell lies the curved headwall of Craig Pwllfa, behind which is the plateau of Waun Rydd (SO 0620). The latter attains a height of 769m. In the cirque below the headwall is a magnificent crescentic glacial moraine (Photo 11). It comprises mainly angular stones, some of which are striated, in finer sediment. Some hummocks occur inside the moraine but do not form a well-defined inner moraine. A snowbed origin has been suggested for these hummocks, but formation by a retreating glacier seems more likely. The cirque faces north-east making it shaded and ideally oriented for receiving wind-drifted snow.

## Cwm Cwareli

Literally the 'quarry valley', this north-facing valley does not possess well-marked depositional features. However, mounds or ridges of debris down to an altitude of 520m have been noted. Two ridges have been recognised, the outer one being the more distinct with a height of up to 4m. The source of rocks in the ridges has been traced to exposures of bedrock in the headwall. Formation at the foot of a snowbed has been suggested, but the large distance of the ridges from the backwall and their broad v-shaped plan form indicate a glacial origin, despite the lack of reports of striated rock fragments.

## Cwm Oergwm

Cwm Oergwm (Figure 15), literally the 'cold valley', has a fine set of depositional ridges. There is a clear outer ridge (SO 043204) (1 in Figure 15) which is broadly v-shaped in plan form and stretches

*Photo 11: Cwm Pwllfa moraine, Brecon Beacons.*

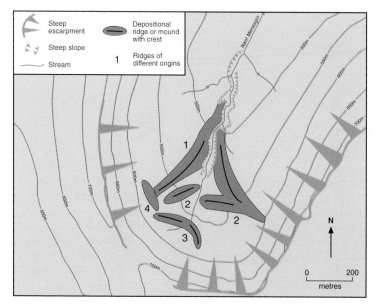

*Figure 15: Cwm Oergwm showing depositional features. Numbers indicate ridges and mounds referred to in the text.*

a distance of about 550m downvalley. Inside this ridge, there are two short ridge fragments (2) on both sides of the Nant Menasgin that more or less parallel the outer ridge. There can be little doubt that both these features are glacial moraines. In addition, nestling almost against the base of the headwall are two other landforms; a prominent crescentic ridge (3) (SO 041200) that encloses a peaty hollow and faces north-east and a less distinct ridge (4) that appears to sit on a small bedrock bench some way up the western scarp. Because of its arcuate form, ridge 3 is thought to be a glacial moraine, although a snowbed origin has also been suggested. Ridge 4 (SO 038202), on the other hand, could well be a pronival rampart as it is of the right order of size in relation to the scarp and in a characteristic position (i.e. on the footslope of the scarp).

## Cwm Cynwyn

This valley lies immediately west of Cwm Oergwm, is likewise north-facing and has steep sides. The top of the backwall varies in altitude from nearly 800m in the west down to about 600m before rising again to about 720m in the east. Two clear depositional ridges can be found here. The larger one (SO 034213) stretches across the valley down to about 420m. It has been cut through by the stream which follows a dog-leg route. Upstream of this ridge, the ground is hummocky but nowhere can clear ridges be seen. Near the head of the valley, however, a further distinct ridge (SO 033209) encloses a peaty area.

The glacial origin of the lower ridge is virtually beyond question but the origin of the upper ridge is less clear. Although regarded in the past as a pronival rampart, it is far more likely to be a glacial moraine in view mainly of its arcuate form and appreciable distance from the backwall.

## Cwm Sere

Previous writers have argued that this north-facing valley does not contain any moraines or pronival ramparts. If this is so, the reason may lie in the fact that the ground to the west is broken up by steep scarps which would intercept much of the snow that would otherwise have reached Cwm Sere. On the other hand, there is an indistinct set of hummocks (SO 021218) broadly aligned across the valley floor at an altitude of about 500m, which could have been deposited by glacier ice. The absence of any features nearer the headwall, as seen in neighbouring valleys, could simply be a result of destruction or overriding by large amounts of talus and impressive debris cones.

## Cwm Llwch

A magnificent crescentic glacial moraine (SO 003221) (Photo 12) nestles beneath the western curved section of the long scarp formed by Craig Cwm Llwch, which runs north-west from Corn Du. The moraine, which dams the shallow lake known as Llyn Cwm Llwch (less than 6m deep), is composed of several superimposed ridges rising to some 18m. In the nineteenth century, Reade (1894) first commented on it; he was struck by the favourable shaded position of the former glacier. The site is also, of course, well positioned to receive snow blown off the sloping ground to the west. It has been suggested that broad indistinct hummocky ground east of this moraine complex represents another older moraine, but this remains conjectural. The moraine is large in relation to the glacier, suggesting that the glacier was very active and/or that there was a plentiful supply of debris.

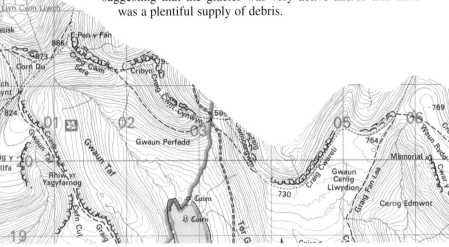

***Photo 12: The Cwm Llwch moraine,*** *which dams a shallow lake (Llyn Cwm Llwch).*

## Pen Milan

In a tributary cirque about 700m north-west of Llyn Cwm Llwch, there is an outer curved depositional ridge (SN 998227) rising 3-6m above the level of the bedrock bench on which it sits. The headwall rises to about 120m above the cirque floor. The northerly aspect of the cirque means that it is shaded and was well positioned for receiving wind-drifted snow from the west during the Loch Lomond Stadial. A glacial origin seems established given the crescentic form of the ridge, the ample cross-sectional depth at the site for the glacier ice development and the presence of striated rock fragments in the ridge.

## Cwm Crew

Immediately west of Blaen Taf Fechan lies the steep, narrow Crew Valley (Photo 13). Its valley head is an almost complete amphitheatre with, on its western side, the steep crags of Craig y Byllfa (SO 006198) which are about 45m high. At the northern end, part of the headwall has slumped (SO 007204), probably for the same reasons as the more spectacular collapse at Craig Cerrig-gleisiad. A magnificent eastern depositional ridge comprising angular and subangular, occasionally striated rock fragments in fine sediment increases in size in a southerly direction until it is some 15m high where it meets the stream. West of the stream, the ridge (SO 007196) climbs upslope towards the southernmost limit of the crags. The valley floor inside this outer ridge is hummocky in places. This topography may consist of glacial sediments laid down as the glacier wasted. At first glance, this is not a promising site for perennial snowbed let alone glacier development, as it faces south (and

**Photo 13: Oblique aerial photograph of Cwm Crew moraine.** *Copyright: Cambridge Air Photo Collection.*

therefore experiences little shading) and lacks an impressive escarpment. Yet it seems fairly certain that the cwm was occupied by a glacier during the Loch Lomond Stadial in view of the lobate plan form of the ridge, its extension downvalley, the continuance of the ridge right up the eastern crags, the downvalley increase in size of the eastern ridge and its content of striated rock fragments. Had the ridge been formed at the foot of a snowbed, one would expect a pronival rampart only to have formed under the escarpment where frost-shattered material could have moved down the snowbed's surface. In addition, it is inconceivable that the west ridge could have been formed in this way and this seems to confirm its glacial heritage. That a glacier formed in this south-facing valley demonstrates the effectiveness here of snow nourishment by wind-drifting despite the absence of shading.

## Blaen Taf Fechan

Two sets of depositional ridges and hummocks occur on the western side of this valley upstream of Neuadd Reservoirs: one lies below the steep escarpment of Craig Gwaun Taf (SO 008204), while the other occurs east of Cefn Cul (SO 013194) (Figure 14). There are no depositional features below the intervening, more degraded stretch of escarpment (Photo 14) and, since it borders the eastern (i.e. downwind) side of the Cwm Crew depression, this part of Blaen Taf Fechan must have been comparatively starved of wind-

*Photo 14: Looking southwards down the western side of Blaen Taf Fechan. Note how the near and far ends of the escarpment are steep where the Craig Gwaun Taf and Cefn Cul glaciers were active but comparatively degraded between these locations. This degraded section had no glacier because it was relatively starved of wind-drifted snow, which instead accumulated below Craig y Byllfa to the west (behind the escarpment in this photograph) and nourished the Cwm Crew glacier.*

drifted snow from the west (see Figure 4). Yet again, therefore, there is clear evidence of the significance of wind-drifted snow and of a south-westerly wind direction in nourishing and maintaining glaciers and snowbeds. The more northerly of the two sets of features (below Craig Gwaun Taf) is indistinct when seen from the escarpment, in part because the features are dissected by later erosion but mainly because the eroded blocks of **blanket peat** catch the eye rather than the underlying depositional landforms. Seen from the valley floor, however, the dissected hummocks form two lines that continue up to the escarpment at the southern end. Northwards they become increasingly difficult to trace.

East of Cefn Cul, on a bedrock bench opposite a marked escarpment indentation, lies a curved ridge complex (SO 016196). It peters out with ill-defined hummocks to the south. Its curved form, the large distance from the central part of the ridges to the escarpment foot (more than 200m), and low angle from ridge to escarpment top indicate a glacial origin. In detail, the moraine is made up of short cusp-shaped ridge sections. One view is that continuation of the ridge complex southwards beyond the escarpment indentation indicates that the glacier moved predominantly south-eastwards along the escarpment (Carr, 2001). Although the ground falls away in this direction, other evidence clearly indicates only easterly movement of the glacier in a fan-like fashion away from the headwall. This is reflected in the changing orientation of individual depositional ridge sections along the moraine and the lack of any sign of a lateral moraine climbing at least partway up the escarpment near the southern end of the indentation, as is the case for the moraines, for example, in Cwm Crew and at the foot of Fan Hir in the Mynydd Du (page 30), where there was clearly some glacier movement more or less parallel to the escarpment as well as away from it.

At the southern end of Graig Fan Ddu near a cairn lies a previously unreported depositional ridge (SO 022183) partially enclosing an escarpment indentation. It is indistinct and should not be confused with the large mounds farther downslope reflecting the underlying bedrock. Its origin is unclear.

## Access

The easiest access to the western sites (Pen Milan, Cwm Llwch, Cwm Crew and the two main features described in Taf Fechan (Craig Gwaun Taf and Cefn Cul)) is by a footpath beginning at a car park by the A470 at SN 987198. There are additional points of access from limited roadside parking about 1km south of Upper Neuadd Reservoir at SO 032179, from where there is a footpath leading to Cwm Cynwyn, and from a car park at SO 056176, from where a path leads up to Craig y Fan Ddu (SO 054185).

# GLOSSARY

**Arcuate.** Possessing an arc-like or curved form.

**Blanket peat.** A veneer up to a few metres thick of peat typical of wet upland areas in Britain. Many blanket bogs show evidence of erosion.

**BP** (as in years BP). Before the present (for consistency taken as AD 1950). It is a term widely used in reporting radiocarbon dates.

**Cirque** (also **corrie**). A steep-walled armchair-shaped rock hollow enlarged by the erosive action of a glacier located within it.

**Debris cone.** A cone-shaped accumulation of rock material often found at the base of a gully or debris chute below steep rock surfaces.

**Debris chute.** A gully high on a steep mountain side down which freeze-thaw weathered debris falls, slides or moves rapidly as a debris flow.

**Debris flow.** On a steep rock or talus slope, the rapid downslope flow of a slurry made up of water and a mixture of sizes of rock material, and the resulting landform (usually a channel with lateral ridges and an end lobe or fan).

**Erratic.** A piece of rock carried by a glacier or ice-sheet and deposited in an area of dissimilar geology (from Latin *errare* meaning to go astray).

**Freeze-thaw weathering.** The penetration of rock joints, bedding planes and pores by water which then freezes and expands, causing the rock to break up.

**Interstadial.** A brief interval (perhaps only a few hundred years, in some cases) of relatively mild conditions within a glacial phase, which is much shorter than an interglacial.

**Kettle hole.** A near-circular or more elongated, enclosed depression in glacial deposits, formed when a body of ice is detached, buried in sediments and subsequently melts to produce a collapse of the overlying material.

**Moraine.** An accumulation of material (ranging potentially from boulders to clay in size) forming a ridge or a series of ridges or hummocks. In the case of the type of moraine described in this guide, the material would have been transported by a glacier or ice-sheet and usually dumped or bulldozed into position along the ice margin.

**Periglacial.** Refers to the climate, processes and landforms of any area not only adjacent to an ice-sheet but also any area subject to a cold climate where freeze-thaw weathering of rock is important.

**Pronival (protalus) rampart.** A ridge or ramp of mainly coarse angular debris formed at the downslope margin of a perennial snowbed.

**Run-out.** Refers in rock avalanches to the flowage of rock debris over comparatively large distances as a result of favourable site characteristics.

**Slopewash.** Sediment removed by running water moving as a sheet or in small channels (rills) over a slope.

**Stadial.** An interval of cold climate shorter in length than a full glacial episode.

**Striations** (also **striae**). Scratches or small grooves found on ice-scoured bedrock surfaces or rock fragments subject, respectively, to scratching by rock fragments embedded in the base of a sliding glacier/ice sheet or particle-to-particle contact.

**Talus.** An accumulation of angular rock debris of variable size at the foot of a cliff or steep slope.

**Trough head.** A steep-sided glacial valley ending abruptly upvalley in a steep headwall. Brecon Beacons trough heads are likely to have been excavated mainly during glacial phases when they were occupied by valley glaciers or fast-moving ice streams within an ice-sheet cover, and not during the Loch Lomond Stadial.

**Tundra.** The sub-Arctic plain – a treeless region now confined mostly to latitudes beyond 60°N, experiencing long cold winters with mean annual temperatures as low as -10°C.

**Warm-based glacier.** A glacier in which the basal temperature is sufficiently high for meltwater to be present so that the glacier can move by sliding over the ground as well as by the ice deforming.

# BIBLIOGRAPHY

Bowen, D.Q. (1999) 'Wales' in Bowen, D.Q. (ed) *A Revised Correlation of Quaternary Deposits in the British Isles*. Geological Society Special Report No. 23. Bath: British Geological Society Publishing House.

Campbell, S. and Bowen, D.Q. (1989) *The Quaternary of Wales*. Geological Conservation Review Series. Peterborough: Nature Conservancy Council.

Carr, S. (2001) 'A glaciological approach for the discrimination of Loch Lomond Stadial glacial landforms in the Brecon Beacons, South Wales', *Proceedings of the Geologists' Association*, 112, pp. 253-62.

Clark, J.M. and Lewis, W.V. (1951) 'Rotational movement in cirque and valley glaciers', *Journal of Geology*, 59, pp. 546-66.

Ellis-Gruffydd, I.D. (1972) *The Glacial Geomorphology of the Upper Usk Basin (South Wales), and its Right Bank Tributaries*. Unpublished PhD thesis, University of London.

Ellis-Gruffydd, I.D. (1977) 'Late Devensian glaciation in the Upper Usk Basin', *Cambria*, 4, 1, pp. 46-55.

Evans, I.S. (1999) 'Was the cirque glaciation of Wales time-transgressive or not?', *Annals of Glaciology*, 28, pp. 33-9.

Howard, F.T. (1901) 'Observations on lakes and tarns of South Wales', *Transactions of the Cardiff Naturalists' Society*, 32, pp. 29-43.

Isarin, R.F.B., Renssen, H and Vandenberghe, J. (1998) 'The impact of the North Atlantic Ocean on the Younger Dryas climate in northwestern and central Europe', *Journal of Quaternary Science*, 13, pp. 447-53.

Lewis, C.A. (1966) *The Periglacial Landforms of the Brecon Beacons, Wales*. Unpublished PhD thesis, University of Ireland.

Lewis, C.A. (1970) 'The glaciations of the Brecknock Beacons, Wales', *Brycheiniog*, 14, pp. 97-120.

Moore, J.J. (1970) 'Appendix: the pollen diagram for Mynydd Illtud' in Lewis, C.A. (ed) *The Glaciations of Wales and Adjoining Regions*. London: Longman, pp. 168-73.

Reade, T.M. (1894) 'The moraine of Llyn Cwm Llwch on the Brecon Beacons', *Proceedings of the Liverpool Geological Society*, 7, pp. 270-6.

Robertson, D.W. (1989) *Aspects of the Late-glacial and Flandrian Environmental History of the Brecon Beacons, Fforest Fawr, Black Mountain, South Wales with Emphasis on the Late-glacial and Early Flandrian Periods*. Unpublished PhD thesis, University of Wales.

Robertson, T. (ed) (1933) *The Geology of the South Wales Coalfield. Part V. The Country Around Merthyr Tydfil*. Memoir of the Geological Survey of Great Britain. London: HMSO.

Shakesby, R.A. (1990) 'Landforms of glacial and fluvioglacial deposition' in Stephens, N. (ed) *Natural Landscapes of Britain from the Air*. Cambridge: Cambridge University Press, pp. 78-113.

Shakesby R.A. (1997) 'Pronival (protalus) ramparts: a review of forms, processes, diagnostic criteria and palaeoenvironmental implications', *Progress in Physical Geography*, 21, pp. 394-418.

Shakesby, R.A. and Matthews, J.A. (1993) 'The Loch Lomond Stadial at Fan Hir, Mynydd Du (Brecon Beacons), South Wales: critical evidence and palaeoclimatic implications', *Geological Journal*, 28, pp. 69-79.

Shakesby, R.A. and Matthews, J.A. (1996) 'Glacial activity and paraglacial landsliding activity in the Devensian Lateglacial: evidence from Craig Cerrig-gleisiad and Fan Dringarth, Fforest Fawr (Brecon Beacons), South Wales', *Geological Journal*, 31, pp. 143-58.

Statham, I. (1976) 'Debris flows on vegetated screes in the Black Mountain, Carmarthenshire', *Earth Surface Processes*, 1, pp. 173-80.

Thomas, T.M. (1959) 'The geomorphology of Brecknock', *Brycheiniog*, 5, pp. 55-156.

Trotman, D.M. (1964) *Data for Late-glacial and Post-glacial Vegetation History in South Wales*. Unpublished PhD thesis, University of Wales.

Walker, M.J.C. (1980) 'Late-glacial history of the Brecon Beacons, South Wales', *Nature*, 287, pp. 133-5.

Walker, M.J.C. (1982a) 'The late-glacial and early Flandrian deposits at Traeth Mawr, Brecon Beacons, South Wales', *New Phytologist*, 90, pp. 177-94.

Walker, M.J.C. (1982b) 'Early and mid-Flandrian environmental history of the Brecon Beacons, South Wales', *New Phytologist*, 91, pp. 147-65.

Whittow, J.B. (1992) *Geology and Scenery in Britain*. London: Chapman and Hall.